Universal Edition

Take another ten

for clarinet and piano

arranged by James Rae

Triangle Pianos
SOUTHAMPTON
023 8055 2656

www.**universale**dition.com
vienna · london · new york

UE 21 169

ISMN: M-008-06751-8
UPC 8-03452-01609-0
ISBN 3-7024-1893-8

Contents

Preface

Following on from the success of the original Take Ten series, Take Another Ten is a further collection of popular concert pieces for the intermediate player. Once again I have chosen a wide range of compositional styles ranging from Bach to the present day which I feel will demonstrate the great versatility of the instrument. The accompaniments have been designed to be both approachable and musically supportive. I have also included chord symbols to enable the pianist to elaborate on the written accompaniment.

Vorwort

Auf den Erfolg der ersten Reihe Take Ten folgt nun eine weitere Sammlung von beliebten Konzertstücken für fortgeschrittene Spieler: Take Another Ten. Wiederum habe ich mich für eine breite Palette von Kompositionsstilen von Bach bis zum heutigen Tag entschieden, da ich glaube, dass dadurch die große Vielseitigkeit des Instruments am besten zum Ausdruck kommt. Die Begleitungen wurden so geschrieben, dass sie sowohl leicht zu spielen sind als auch musikalische Unterstützung liefern. Ich habe zudem Akkordsymbole hinzugefügt, um dem Pianisten die Möglichkeit zu geben, seine eigenen Ausarbeitungen anzufertigen.

Préface

Après le succès remporté par la première série Take Ten, le recueil Take Another Ten, rassemble de nouveaux morceaux de concert célèbres destinés aux instrumentistes de niveau moyen. J'ai sélectionné ici encore un large éventail de styles s'étendant de Bach à la musique actuelle qui souligne la grande diversité d'expression de l'instrument. Les accompagnements ont été conçus d'accès facile tout en fournissant un solide soutien musical. J'ai également inséré des chiffrages d'accord pour donner au pianiste la possibilité d'enrichir l'accompagnement écrit.

James Rae

Where is Love

Lionel Bart
(1930–1999)
Arr. James Rae

© 1959 Lakeview Music Publishing Co.Ltd
of Suite 2.07, Plaza 535 King's Road, London SW10 0SZ
International Copyright Secured. All Rights Reserved. Used by Permission.
This edition © Copyright 2003 by Universal Edition (London) Ltd., London.

UE 21 169 L

Le Petit Nègre

Claude Debussy
(1862–1918)
Arr. James Rae

UE 21 169 L

Moonlight Serenade

Mitchell Parrish
and Glenn Miller

Arr. James Rae

UE 21 169 L

Ice 'n' Slice

James Rae

UE 21 169 L

Anitra's Dance
(from Peer Gynt)

Edvard Grieg
(1843–1907)
Arr. James Rae

UE 21 169 L

Speak Low
(from "One Touch Of Venus")

Kurt Weill
(1900–1950)
Arr. James Rae

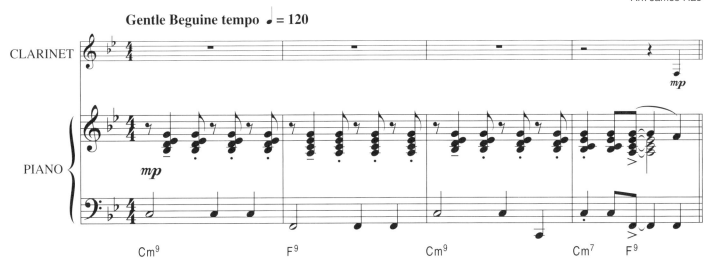

UE 21 169 L

14

Ragtime Dance

Scott Joplin
(1868–1917)
Arr. James Rae

UE 21 169 L

Hava Nagila

Jewish Traditional
Arr. James Rae

UE 21 169 L

Ave Verum Corpus

Wolfgang Amadeus Mozart
(1756–1791)
Arr. James Rae

UE 21 169 L

Minuet in G minor

Johann Sebastian Bach
(1685–1750)
Arr. James Rae